A little head peeped out from behind the rhinoceros. Alfie saw a baby rhino. She wanted to play.

'I am sad,' said Alfie. 'I am all by myself. I have lost my elephant family. Have you seen them?'

'They may be down by the river,' said the mother rhinoceros. 'Come with us and we will help you find them.'

Alfie and the rhinos went across the grassy land of Africa to the river. They did not see the elephants.

Alfie was thirsty. He fell into the water. He had a big drink. He splashed water all over himself.

The rhinos watched Alfie from the riverbank. He went into the middle of the river. He loved the cool water.

Then Alfie began to sink. His head went under the water. Only the tip of his trunk was above the water.

The baby rhino ran up and down the riverbank.
'Help, help,' she shouted. 'Alfie is sinking in the
water.'